ISABEL THOMAS

BUILD YOUR OWN BODY

GET READY FOR AN ADVENTURE!

Have you ever wanted to find out how your brilliant body works?
What do you think you'd need?

CHECKLIST

X	X	X	✔
Stethoscope	X-ray machine	Years of training	THIS BOOK AND A PAIR OF SCISSORS

You don't need to use X-rays to get to know your body inside out. This book is packed with activities that you can do at home, using every page in a different way.

It's not one of those Zzzzzzzz activity books that's all about sitting quietly and labelling pictures of teeth. This book bites back!

Get ready to tear, fold, cut, construct and experiment... but be warned:

THIS BOOK WILL SELF-DESTRUCT!

BLOOMSBURY
Activity Books

HOW TO ~~USE~~ THIS BOOK
WRECK

The human body is an amazing place. Get ready to discover the strange secrets lurking inside. You can choose your own route, but where will you start?

EXPLORE YOUR BRAIN (PAGE 30)

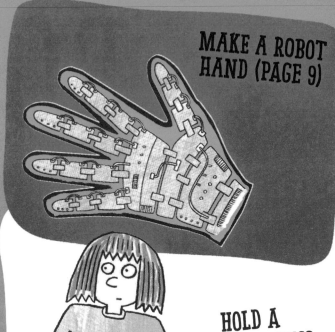

MAKE A ROBOT HAND (PAGE 9)

DISCOVER THE SECRET OF LIFE (PAGE 62)

HOLD A FINGERLYMPICS (PAGE 49)

TRAINING CAMP

 Cut the paper along these lines

Fold the paper along these lines

 Glue here

Look out for this icon — these pages will completely self-destruct, so make sure you read every word before getting started!

WARNING! THIS PAGE WILL SELF-DESTRUCT!

SAFETY INFORMATION

The projects in this book have been designed to be safe for you to carry out at home if you follow the instructions carefully. We recommend that you get adult help for certain projects, including Build A Body and Map Your Tongue. When carrying out the activities in this book, avoid placing your fingers or any other objects into your eyes, ears or nose, and check with an adult that the foods you would like to use for the Map Your Tongue activity are safe to put in your mouth.

Extra kit

Before you set off, grab some scissors, glue, sticky tape and colouring pencils — most projects use these. Look out for boxes like this to find out if you need to pack any extra kit.

DANCING BONES

Make a moving skeleton to learn about the main bones in the body.

Extra kit:

- Scissors
- 15 paper fasteners
- Hole punch
- Fine thread
- Wooden skewer or short stick
- Thin card
- Glue stick

What to do:

1. Cut out the skeleton sections on the back of this page. Glue them on to a piece of thin card.

2. When the glue is dry, punch a hole in each marked spot. Use the paper fasteners to join the bones.

3. Tape a short length of thread to the back of the skull. Tie the other end around the stick.

4. Wrap a long length of thread around the paper fasteners at each elbow and knee joint.

5. Tie the other end of these threads on to the stick. Make sure the thread is long enough for your skeleton's arms and legs to hang down.

6. Make your skeleton dance by twitching and pulling the threads!

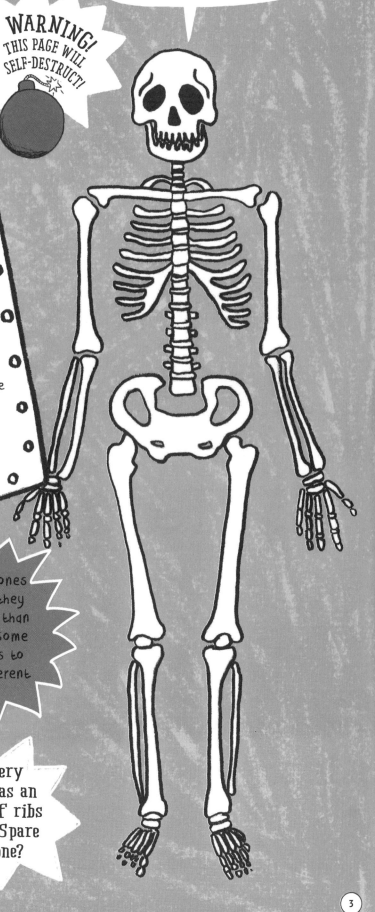

Bones are a bit like scaffolding for your body. Unlike scaffolding they can repair themselves if they are damaged. They also protect your squishiest organs, and act as blood factories.

WARNING! THIS PAGE WILL SELF-DESTRUCT!

Joints link your bones together. Luckily they are more advanced than paper fasteners. Some joints allow bones to move in many different directions.

You missed the party.

I had no body to go with.

One in every 20 people has an extra pair of ribs — or two. Spare ribs, anyone?

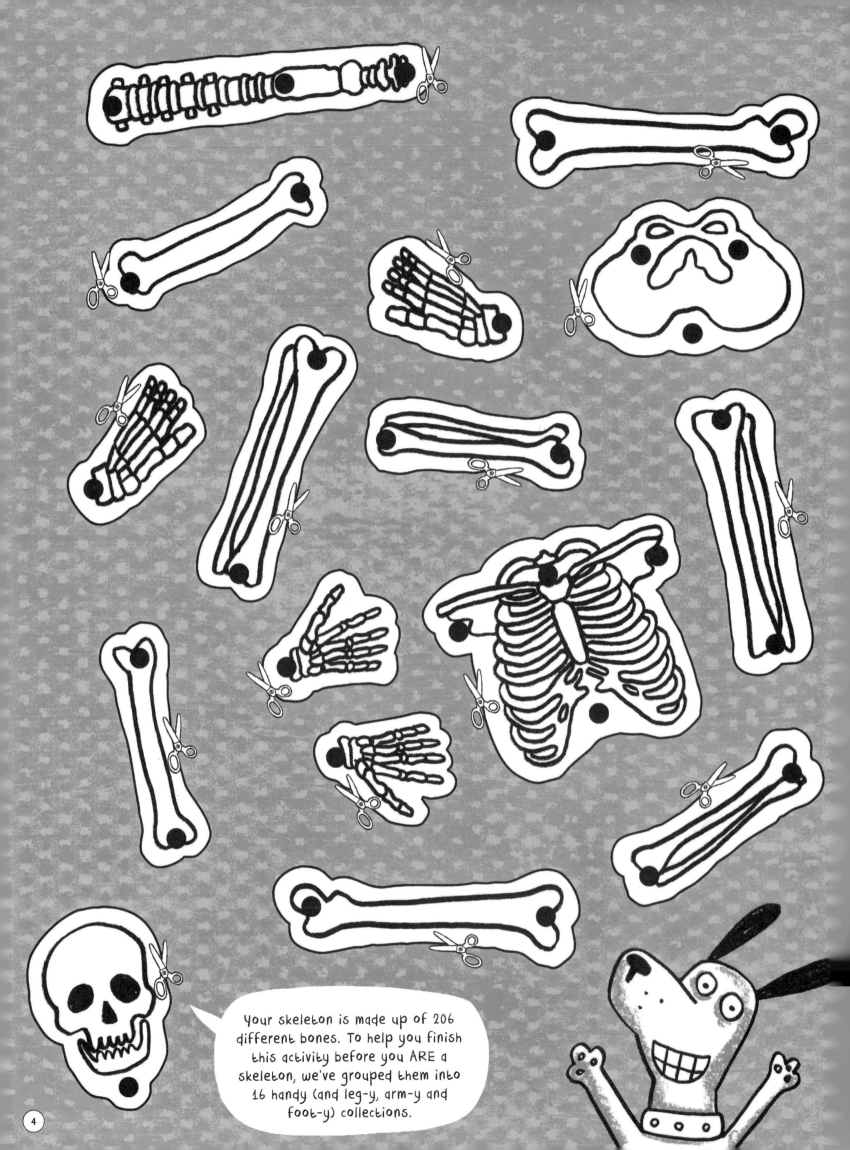

Your skeleton is made up of 206 different bones. To help you finish this activity before you ARE a skeleton, we've grouped them into 16 handy (and leg-y, arm-y and foot-y) collections.

4

MAKE A SUPERHERO

Think of your body systems as superheroes with special powers. They work together to keep the world's most important person alive – you!

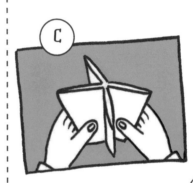

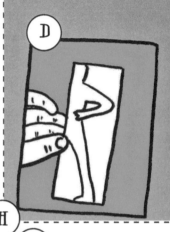

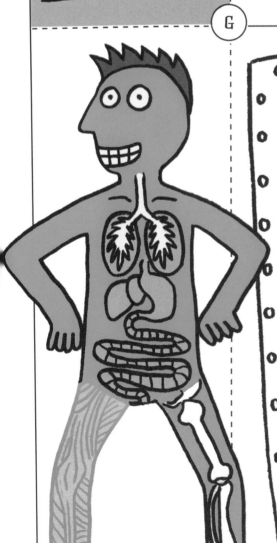

Extra kit:

- Scissors
- Glue stick

What to do:

1. Remove this page from the book.

2. Fold along all the dashed lines, in both directions (A).

3. Open the paper out. Carefully cut along the solid line from G to H.

4. Put a thin layer of glue on flaps I and J, and fold the paper in half from top to bottom.

5. Grip one of the short edges in each hand, and bring your hands together so the middle section opens up to form a diamond (B).

6. Dab a little glue inside the diamond, and keep bringing your hands together until the paper touches (C).

7. Flatten the paper. When the glue is dry, cut around the body shape (D, E).

8. Stand your action figure on a table and explore some of your body systems (F)!

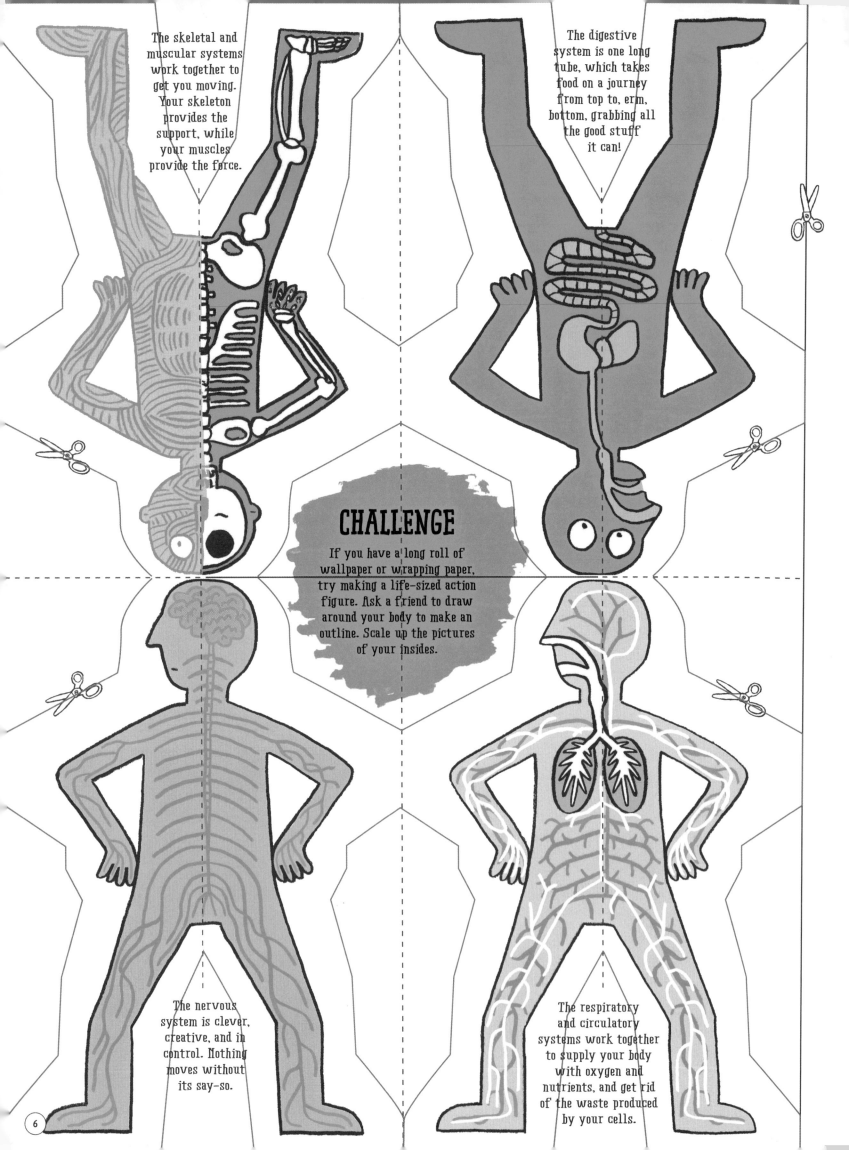

The skeletal and muscular systems work together to get you moving. Your skeleton provides the support, while your muscles provide the force.

The digestive system is one long tube, which takes food on a journey from top to, erm, bottom, grabbing all the good stuff it can!

CHALLENGE

If you have a long roll of wallpaper or wrapping paper, try making a life-sized action figure. Ask a friend to draw around your body to make an outline. Scale up the pictures of your insides.

The nervous system is clever, creative, and in control. Nothing moves without its say-so.

The respiratory and circulatory systems work together to supply your body with oxygen and nutrients, and get rid of the waste produced by your cells.

HOW TO BUILD A BODY

Imagine if you came with a list of ingredients. Top of the list would be oxygen, carbon, hydrogen and nitrogen. These four elements are the main building blocks of EVERY living thing.

Hmmm! Carbohydrates are my favourite!

An average 10-year-old contains around:

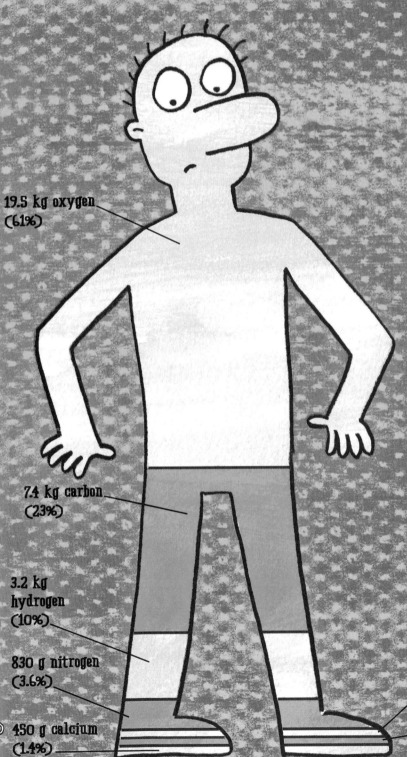

19.5 kg oxygen (61%)

7.4 kg carbon (23%)

3.2 kg hydrogen (10%)

830 g nitrogen (3.6%)

450 g calcium (1.4%)

350 g phosphorus (1.1%)

350 g other substances (1.1%)

Extra kit:
- Scissors
- Small, transparent plastic bags
- Sticky tape

What to do:
1. Cut this page out of the book. Go on a treasure hunt to find examples of the main materials that make up your body.
2. Stick the samples you find into the lab overleaf (page 8). Can you collect them all?

To complete the recipe, collect the 13 elements that make up most of your body. Some are only found in tiny amounts, but each is vital for survival! As your body grows, you need to top up on the ingredients by eating a wide range of food.

WARNING! THIS PAGE WILL SELF-DESTRUCT!

STICK YOUR SAMPLES HERE!

OXYGEN

Most of the oxygen in your body is in the form of water – almost three-quarters of your body is water.

HYDROGEN

Hydrogen is the other element that combines with oxygen to make water. Add hydrogen and oxygen to your collection by sealing a drop of water inside a plastic bag and sticking it here.

CARBON

Carbon is an important building block of all living things (and things that used to be alive, such as this page!). Diamonds and pencil graphite are types of pure carbon. Unless you're extremely rich, you'll probably have to go for the pencil...

NITROGEN

Nitrogen is the main element that makes up air. Trap some air in a small plastic bag and stick it here!

PHOSPHORUS

You'll find phosphorus in baking powder and fine china. Unless you have a VERY understanding great aunt, go for the baking powder.

CALCIUM

Chalk and cheese are more similar than you think: both are full of calcium. Stick a piece of chalk here – it's less smelly than cheese.

SULPHUR

Pure sulphur is bright yellow, and easiest to find near volcanoes. If you don't live next to a volcano, try getting hold of a meteorite or some garlic instead!

POTASSIUM

Foods such as beans and bananas are rich in potassium. Stick a dried red kidney bean here.

CHLORINE

Table salt is made up of two elements – sodium and chlorine. Both are pretty dangerous in pure form, but together they form a chemical safe enough to eat in small quantities.

SODIUM

Our bodies lose salt whenever we sweat or cry, so we need to eat a small amount every day.

IODINE

This is found in some table salt (not sea salt). Stick a sample of table salt here and you'll have all three elements covered.

MAGNESIUM

More than half of the magnesium in our bodies is stored in our bones. Sesame seeds and almonds are both rich in magnesium.

IRON

Iron is an important ingredient in blood. It's also the metal used to make some nails – find a small nail and stick it here.

Did you hear the joke about Frankenstein's monster?

It had me in stitches!

I'VE COLLECTED THEM ALL – CAN I BUILD A NEW ME?

The ingredients may be easy to find, but putting them together is not as simple! As a human grows, the building blocks (from our food) combine in different ways to form thousands of chemicals. These carry out different jobs in your body.

ROBOT HIGH FIVE

Make a robot hand to find out how muscles and tendons work together. Waving goodbye just got interesting!

Extra kit:

- Scissors
- Four drinking straws
- Sticky tape
- String or thread

What to do:

1. Cut out the hand shape below.

2. Cut each straw into four pieces (three 2 cm lengths, and one 7 cm length). Tape the lengths of straw to the white areas on the hand. Use the three leftover pieces for the thumb.

3. Cut five pieces of string, each around 25 cm long. Feed a piece of string through the straws that make up the little finger. Leave 2 cm of thread sticking out at the top. Fold it over and tape it to the top straw.

4. Repeat step 3 for the other fingers and the thumb.

5. Hold the model in one hand, and gather the free lengths of thread in the other hand. Pull all the strings at once to make your model hand wave at you!

Try pulling the strings one at a time to control the fingers.

phalanges

metacarpal bones

carpal bones

radius

ulna

The pieces of straw are like the bones in your hand. Each finger has three bones, called phalanges. Your thumb has two phalanges. Long bones called metacarpals connect your fingers and thumb to your wrist. Joints between the bones allow your fingers to bend.

A real hand is packed with smaller muscles that let you bring your thumb and fingers together, and control how you grip objects. To find out just how fantastic your fingers are, stage a fingerlympics (page 49).

String-like tendons in your arms connect muscles to your fingers. The tendons work like the strings in the model. As the muscles in your arm contract they pull on the tendons. The tendons pull on your fingers, making them bend.

MODEL YOUR MUSCLES

The muscles in your arms make a great team. Make a model arm to find out more.

Extra kit:

- Scissors
- Piece of scrap card
- Two paper fasteners
- String or wool

What to do:

1. Cut out the two arm pieces from the inside front cover.

2. Carefully poke small holes in the three places marked with black spots.

3. Push a paper fastener through the hole at the top of the upper arm, and then through a piece of thin card.

4. Push a second paper fastener through the hole on the lower arm, then through the hole at the bottom of the upper arm, and the thin card. The upper arm will be fixed to the card, but the lower arm should move up and down freely.

5. Bones can't move on their own, so it's time to add muscles. Cut two 20 cm pieces of string or wool. Make a small hole in each of the places marked with a red spot. The hole at the top of the upper arm should also go through the backing card.

6. Feed one end of the string through the hole on the lower arm and tie it in place. Feed the other end through the hole in the upper arm, and the card, so it hangs down behind the card. You could tie a bead on the end to stop it slipping back through the hole.

7. Repeat steps 5 and 6 using the other piece of thread and the pink spots.

8. With your hands behind the card, pull the strings to make the arm move!

Stop winding me up!

Just relax!

Muscles work by getting shorter, and pulling on bones. The pair of strings in the model work like the muscles of your upper arm (the biceps and triceps). These two muscles work together to move your lower arm.

When the biceps muscle contracts (gets shorter), it pulls your lower arm up. When the triceps muscle contracts, your lower arm moves down. When one of these muscles is contracting, the other one MUST relax so it can get longer. If you try to contract both muscles at the same time, your arm stays still!

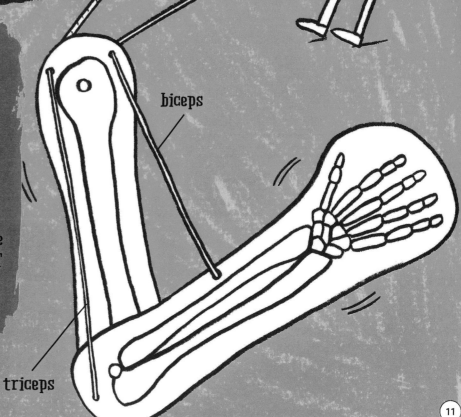

biceps

triceps

YOU'VE BEEN FRAMED

There are more than 7 billion people on Earth, which makes it highly likely that somewhere there is a child who shares your name and strange habits! But in other ways, you are completely unique. Use these pages to record your special features ... it'll be worth a fortune when you're rich and famous!

Extra kit:
- Ink or paint
- Lipstick or tinted lip balm
- Sticky tape
- Coloured pencils
- Colourful food (e.g. blackberries)
- Bronzing powder or eye shadow
- Soft, fluffy make-up brush or paintbrush (for dusting)

What to do:
1. Complete each frame to record some of the features that make you different from everyone else in the world.

FINGERPRINTS

Coat your fingertips with ink (or non-toxic paint) and press here.

LIP PRINT

Brush on some lipstick or tinted lip balm (or eat a really juicy blackberry) and pucker up.

Even identical twins have different fingerprints.

IT WASN'T ME, IT WAS HIM!

The pattern of wrinkles on your lips is as unique as your fingerprints. The science of lip prints even has a name - cheiloscopy. Pucker up!

DNA

Take a piece of hair from your brush or comb and stick it here.

IRIS

Look deep into your eyes and draw what you see.

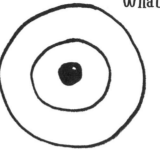

Don't make a spectacle of yourself!

Almost every cell — including hair — contains a copy of your DNA, the instructions for building your entire body! Your DNA is unique (unless you have an identical twin), because half of it comes from your mother and half comes from your father. Even siblings have different combinations.

The colourful part of your eye is called the iris. It's a muscle that contracts and relaxes to change the size of your pupil, and the amount of light entering your eye. The colour of your iris is passed on from your parents, but the patterns are unique.

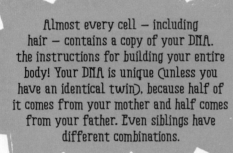

Everyone's tongue has a unique shape and surface texture. Some scientists think that sticking your tongue out could be a great form of identifying people at airports, because it's impossible to forge!

Do you have any ID, Sir?

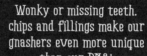

Wonky or missing teeth, chips and fillings make our gnashers even more unique than our DNA!

TONGUE PRINT

Eat a colourful food like blackberries or beetroot, and make a tongue print here.

TEETH

Bite the page gently here (but don't eat it!)

13

TOE PRINTS

Coat a big toe with ink (or non-toxic paint) and press here.

Criminals have been caught using toe prints, which are just as unique as fingerprints.

Did you remember to scrub the toe prints?

SIGNATURE

Scribble your name here.

We are taught to write in the same way as our classmates, but as we get older our handwriting becomes increasingly unique. A signature used to be the main way for a person to identify themselves when withdrawing money from a bank!

EAR PRINT

Brush some bronzing powder or eye shadow on to your ear. Gently push it against the paper. (Don't put anything in your ear.)

The curves and ridges of our ears are so unique that in the near future we may be able to unlock mobile phones simply by holding them up to our ears! Burglars have been caught using ear prints left behind when they put their ear to a window to check that a building sounded empty!

Your smell is also unique to you — but harder to get on to paper!

FOOTPRINTS

Put this page on the floor and walk across it with your shoes on.

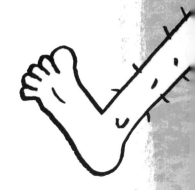

Hiding your face from the camera won't work... we can be identified by the way we walk! Are you sluggish or bouncy? A strider or a shuffler? It's all there in your footprints, and the pressure patterns they leave on the ground.

These features can be very handy to help people prove they are who they say they are. Forensic scientists use these characteristics to help identify people involved in crimes. Forensic evidence can't prove for sure that a person committed a crime, but it can show links between people, places and things.

FINGERPRINT FORENSICS

This page will help you set up your own forensics lab. It's time to find out who's been snooping about in your room!

Extra kit:
- Ink pad (or sponge cloth and paint)

What to do:
1. First, record the fingerprints of your family or friends. Ask each person to dip their fingers in ink and print them across the boxes.

2. Jot down the main details that you notice. Do they have arches, loops or whorls?

You can make your own ink sponge by brushing some thick non-toxic paint on to a sponge cloth. Make a print on scrap paper first, to get rid of excess paint.

KEY FEATURES TO LOOK FOR

The grooved surface of your fingerprints increases the friction between your skin and the objects that you touch — like the tread on a pair of trainers. Natural oils from our skin run into the grooves. When we touch a smooth surface, an oily print of the grooves is left behind. Most fingerprints have one of three patterns — arch, loop or whorl:

YOUR FINGERPRINT DATABASE

NAME	THUMB	INDEX	MIDDLE	RING	LITTLE

THE FORENSICS LAB

Extra kit:
- Scissors
- Clear sticky tape
- Face powder or chalk dust
- Soft, fluffy make-up brush or paintbrush (for dusting)

What to do:
1. Hunt for fingerprints by dusting a smooth object with fine powder. The powder will cling to oily fingerprints, making them easier to see. Dust gently so you don't smudge the evidence!
2. When you spot a fingerprint, carefully place a piece of sticky tape over the top.
3. Peel the tape off and stick it into the lab. The dark background will help you to see the fingerprint clearly. Does it match one of the fingerprints in your database?

Make fine powder by scraping the edge of a spoon along a piece of chalk.

That's NOT what I meant when I asked you to dust your bedroom!

WHICH SIDE ARE YOU ON?

The left side of your brain controls the right side of your body, and vice versa. Confused yet? Let's find out which side is really in charge...

WHICH HAND DO YOU (MAINLY) USE TO CARRY OUT THESE TASKS?

Circle a hand for each.

LEFT		RIGHT
🖐	Writing	🖐
🖐	Drawing	🖐
🖐	Throwing	🖐
🖐	Holding a toothbrush	🖐
🖐	Using scissors	🖐
🖐	Holding a fork	🖐
🖐	Holding a spoon	🖐
🖐	Holding a cup	🖐
🖐	Using a remote control	🖐
🖐	Unscrewing a jar	🖐

Most people find that they perform six to nine of these tasks with just one hand – their dominant hand. If you answered ten 'Right' or ten 'Left', you are strongly right- or left-handed. And if you got half and half? You might be ambidextrous.

The famous artist and inventor Leonardo da Vinci was ambidextrous. He could paint, write and draw equally well with both hands. This is very rare.

CHALLENGE 1

Extra kit:
- Felt tip pen
- Timer

What to do:

1. Hold the pen in your right hand. Starting from the dot, follow the path around the frame as neatly as possible.

2. Swap hands and do the same in the second frame. Which line is neatest?

CHALLENGE 2

Extra kit:
- Felt tip pen
- Timer

What to do:

1. Hold the pen in your right hand. Set a timer for 15 seconds. Follow the trail, putting a small dot in as many circles as possible.

2. Repeat this challenge with the pen in your left hand. Which hand managed to put a dot in most circles?

Try these challenges to find out if you might be ambidextrous too!

Left-hand start

Right-hand start

You probably found that your dominant hand drew most neatly and got further through the maze. Less than 1 in every 100 people can use both hands equally well.

Place a mirror here!

Leonardo da Vinci used mirror writing to record most of his ideas and inventions. Try it yourself. Hold a pen in each hand and place them on the dots below. Write your name backwards and forwards at the same time.

Leonardo da Vinci ⟵ ⟶ Leonardo da Vinci

THINKING IN 3D

What would this page look like if you scrunched it up and rolled it between your hands?

a) Cube-shaped?   b) Ball-shaped?   c) Cat-shaped?

Your brain is brilliant at imagining what objects would look like if they were folded, twisted or turned. Scientists call this spatial reasoning, which means thinking in 3D. It's useful for reading maps, making objects, playing sport, and not bumping into lampposts. Use this puzzle to test your friends and family.

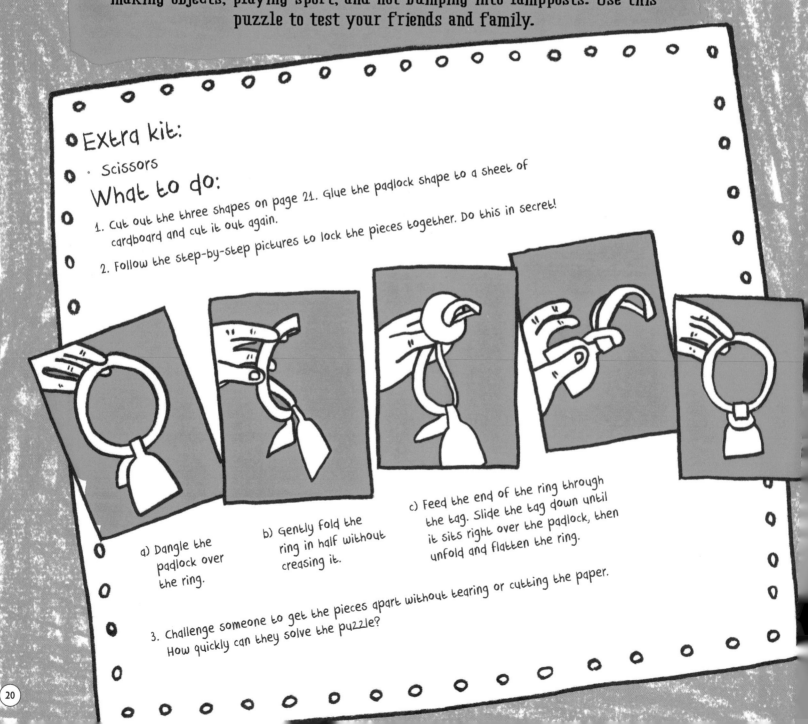

Extra kit:

• Scissors

What to do:

1. Cut out the three shapes on page 21. Glue the padlock shape to a sheet of cardboard and cut it out again.

2. Follow the step-by-step pictures to lock the pieces together. Do this in secret!

a) Dangle the padlock over the ring.

b) Gently fold the ring in half without creasing it.

c) Feed the end of the ring through the tag. Slide the tag down until it sits right over the padlock, then unfold and flatten the ring.

3. Challenge someone to get the pieces apart without tearing or cutting the paper. How quickly can they solve the puzzle?

WARNING!
THIS PAGE WILL
SELF-DESTRUCT!

It's time to put your own spatial reasoning to the test! Follow the instructions below to make three different paper loops. Can you predict what will happen when you cut each one in half?

Cut all the way along the dotted line to cut each strip in half.

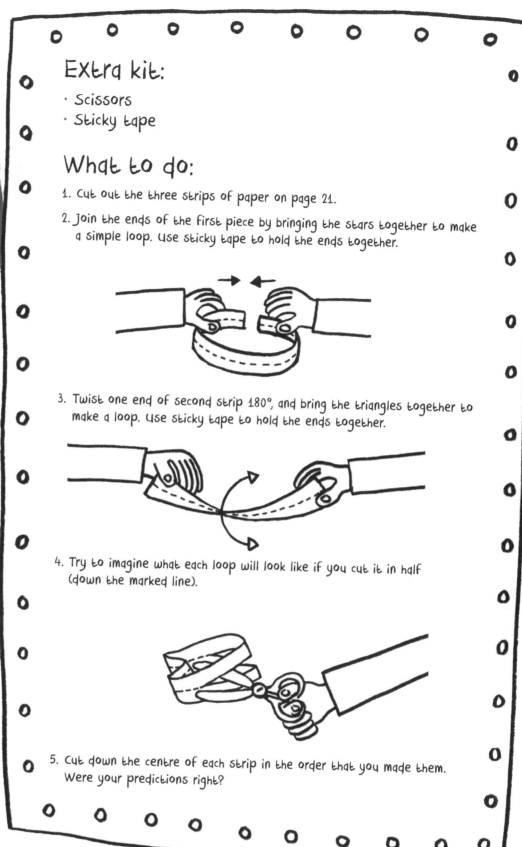

Extra kit:

· Scissors
· Sticky tape

What to do:

1. Cut out the three strips of paper on page 21.

2. Join the ends of the first piece by bringing the stars together to make a simple loop. Use sticky tape to hold the ends together.

3. Twist one end of second strip 180°, and bring the triangles together to make a loop. Use sticky tape to hold the ends together.

4. Try to imagine what each loop will look like if you cut it in half (down the marked line).

5. Cut down the centre of each strip in the order that you made them. Were your predictions right?

By twisting the paper once, you turned a two-sided piece of paper into a one-sided object. It's known as a Mobius strip. Trace around the Mobius strip with your finger and you'll find that the cats can now catch the mice — they are all running on the same surface!

CHALLENGE

Use the third strip of paper to make a third loop, twisting one end 360° before joining it to the other end. Can you predict what will happen when you cut down the central line? Try it and see!

HOW DO YOU DOODLE?

Doodles are drawings we do without thinking too much. Some scientists think doodles can reveal our inner thoughts and feelings, and even our personality! See if you agree.

Collect the doodles done by your family and friends, then amaze (or annoy) them with insights into their personality!

Extra kit:

· Pencil

What to do:

1. Use this space to collect your doodles. Don't think about what you're drawing – try collecting doodles while you are speaking on the phone or watching TV.

2. Flip to the next spread to find out what your doodles might mean.

Scientists think that doodling may help you concentrate. Keeping your hands and brain busy stops you daydreaming and helps you focus on the information being collected by your ears. In one study, scientists found that doodlers remembered more than don't-lers!

SILLY SCRIBBLES OR A PEEK INSIDE YOUR BRAIN?

If you're not trying to draw something in particular, how does your brain decide what to put on the paper? Look at the shapes and symbols you have doodled, and find out what they may mean...

animal facing left

friendly. good at remembering birthdays

animal facing right

gets things done. not good at remembering birthdays

feeling lonely

wants to succeed

practical

good at thinking things through

feeling worried

wants to attract someone's attention

sensitive

like your own company

romantic. creative

shows how you feel about home

has a tricky choice to make

doesn't like being criticized

feeling happy

feels trapped (or wants to trap someone!)

feeling happy (or hungry!)

big personality

finds it hard to trust people

hard on yourself

likes to feel safe

loving. looks after friends and family

daydreamer

feeling shy

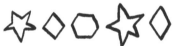
very ambitious

wants things to change

feeling trapped. or have too much to do

wants to move on to new things

IT'S NOT JUST WHAT YOU DRAW, BUT WHERE YOU DRAW IT...

TOP OF PAGE – you may be a daydreamer, with a great imagination. You are good at looking on the bright side of things.

BOTTOM OF PAGE – you may be a hard-working person, who likes to win. You can be quite hard on yourself.

MIDDLE OF PAGE – you may be a careful person, who likes to think things through before acting.

LEFT-HAND SIDE – you may be an introvert, and feel most energetic in your own company.

RIGHT-HAND SIDE – you may be an extrovert, and feel most energetic when you are with other people.

CAN YOU BELIEVE YOUR EYES?

WARNING! THIS PAGE WILL SELF-DESTRUCT!

Would you like to direct a movie? You don't need a ticket to Hollywood — just this page, a drinking straw and your brilliant brain!

Extra kit:

- Scissors
- Drinking straw
- Skewer or knitting needle (that fits easily inside the straw)
- Sticky tape
- Thin card

What to do:

1. Cut out the rectangular templates on this page.
2. Stick the straw to the back of picture a, using the line as a guide (A).
3. Stick the back of picture B to the back of picture a, and to the straw (one side only) (B).
4. Stick the back of picture c to the backs of pictures a and b, and to the straw (C).
5. Slip the straw onto a skewer or knitting needle.
6. Hold the skewer so the cartoon is level with your face. Blow on the paper flaps to make them spin. What do you see?

A   B   C

a

b

c

The person seems to move! This happens because your eyes and brain remember each snapshot for a fraction of a second — long enough for your brain to blend it with the next picture that comes along. This helps your brain to put together an unbroken picture of your surroundings as you move your eyes or head. It also stops the world going black every time you blink!

Persistence of vision also means that you can watch films! Films are made up of thousands of still photographs called frames. If the frames flash up on screen quickly enough, our eyes and brain blend them together to 'see' a moving picture.

And for my next trick... I will use self-destructing science to make colours appear!

Extra kit:

- Scissors
- Drawing pin
- Glue or double-sided sticky tape
- Thin string, wool or cord

What to do:

1. Cut out discs A and B from inside the front cover.
2. Glue discs A and B together, making sure the patterns are on the outside!
3. Rest on something that won't get damaged. Gently push the drawing pin through the dots on one side, to make two small holes. Widen the holes a little with a drawing pin or the point of a pencil.
4. Thread the string through one hole and back through the other. Tie a knot to make a loop around 20 cm long.
5. Ask someone to hold up their index fingers. Loop one end of the string over each finger. Ask your helper to move their fingers apart until the string is taut.
6. Turn the disc to wind the string up. When you let go, the disc should spin quickly. What do you see?

CHALLENGE

Test the spinners under different kinds of light. Try spinning them in different directions. Does anything change?

HOW DOES IT WORK?

Nobody knows! But scientists have a theory. The inside of your eyeballs are lined with cells called cones that detect colours. Blue, red and green light each switch on different cones, which send messages to your brain. Your brain looks at these messages to work out which colours you are seeing. White light is a mixture of every colour, so when you look at the spinning disk, the flashes of white switch on the red and green cones more quickly than the blue cones. The blue cones also stay switched on for longer. This means that the messages saying RED, GREEN and BLUE all arrive at your brain at slightly different times. Your brain thinks you are seeing several different colours!

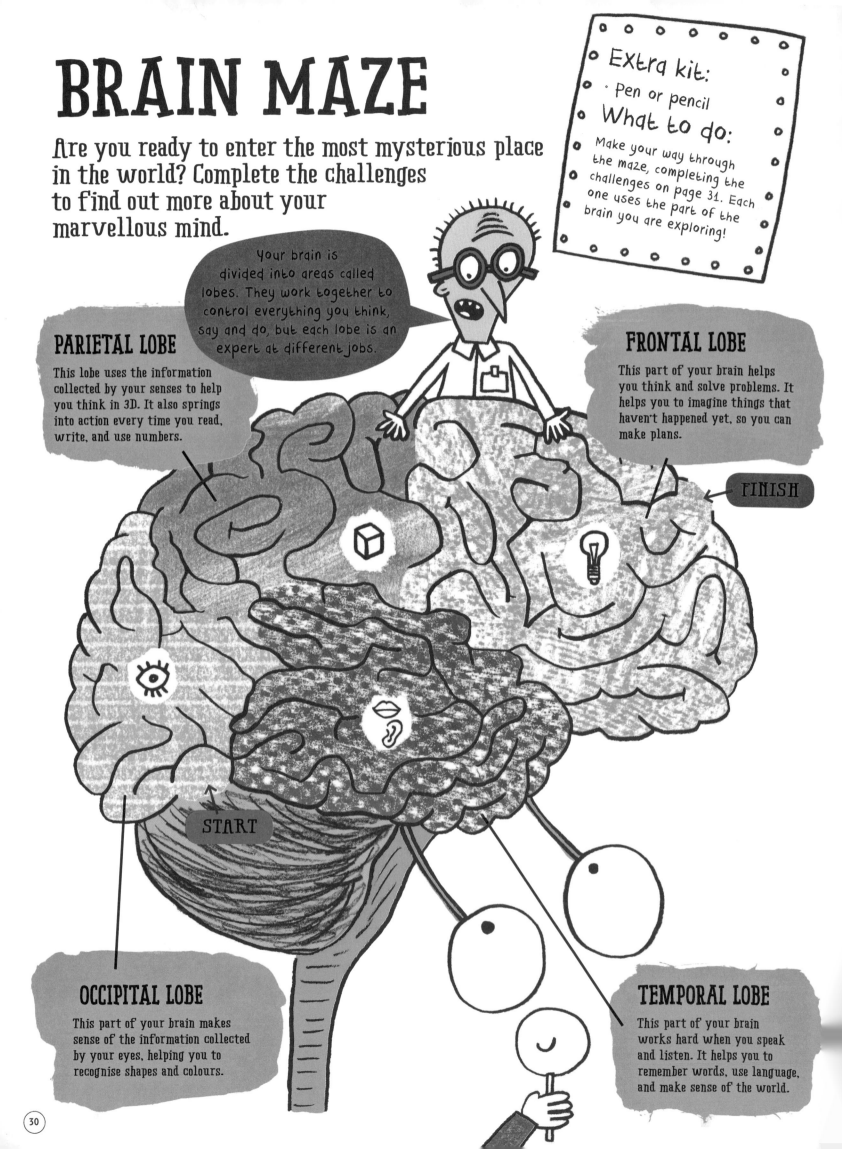

BRAIN MAZE

Are you ready to enter the most mysterious place in the world? Complete the challenges to find out more about your marvellous mind.

Extra kit:
· Pen or pencil

What to do:
Make your way through the maze, completing the challenges on page 31. Each one uses the part of the brain you are exploring!

Your brain is divided into areas called lobes. They work together to control everything you think, say and do, but each lobe is an expert at different jobs.

PARIETAL LOBE

This lobe uses the information collected by your senses to help you think in 3D. It also springs into action every time you read, write, and use numbers.

FRONTAL LOBE

This part of your brain helps you think and solve problems. It helps you to imagine things that haven't happened yet, so you can make plans.

FINISH

START

OCCIPITAL LOBE

This part of your brain makes sense of the information collected by your eyes, helping you to recognise shapes and colours.

TEMPORAL LOBE

This part of your brain works hard when you speak and listen. It helps you to remember words, use language, and make sense of the world.

💡 FRONTAL LOBE
BRAIN CHALLENGE 1: SPOTTING PATTERNS

All of these are Glubbernonks:

None of these is a Glubbernonk:

Which of these are Glubbernonks?

👄 TEMPORAL LOBE
BRAIN CHALLENGE 2: MYSTERY VOWELS

The vowels have been zapped from these body words. Can you work out what they are? (Hint: Try saying them aloud.)

hnds	shldrs	lbws
lgs	hps	stmch
chst	thghs	fngrs
frhd	bck	kns

🧊 PARIETAL LOBE
BRAIN CHALLENGE 3: THINKING IN 3D

Imagine pulling the ends of each tangled rope. Which ropes will end up with knots?

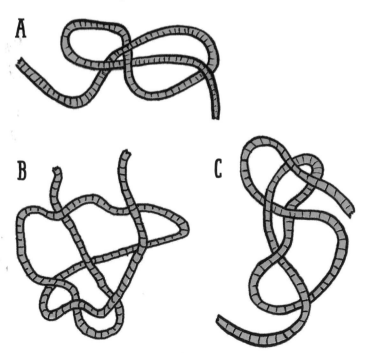

👁 OCCIPITAL LOBE
BRAIN CHALLENGE 4: MAKING SHAPES

Cut out the four shapes below. Fit them together to make a bigger version of the same shape.

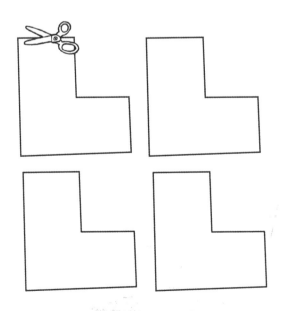

SMELLY-VISION

Find out what your nose knows by creating some smelly art.

Extra kit:

- One or two fresh eggs
- Dried, powdered or liquid foods: the smellier the better!
- Teaspoon
- Water

Try these:
- Ground spices
- Coffee granules
- Cocoa powder
- Powdered milkshake or jelly
- Flavourings such as vanilla extract

What to do:

1. Crack an egg in two and tip the yolk from one half shell to the other, letting the white run out into a bowl.

2. When all of the white has drained away, tip the yolk into a small cup and stir to break it up.

3. Mix half a teaspoon of powdered or dried food with a few drops of water (crush any large lumps first). Add half a teaspoon of egg yolk and mix well. You have made an ancient type of paint, called tempera!

4. Make more paints in the same way. Use them to colour the picture on page 33, or make your own smelly art.

Don't lick your paintings – the egg is not cooked!

Some people have a better sense of smell than others. When your painting is dry, invite your friends and family to sniff your art and see how many smells they can identify.

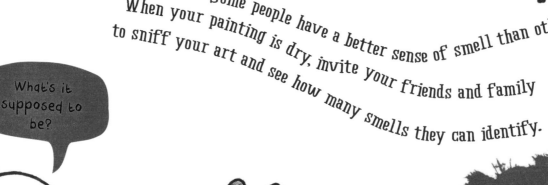

What's it supposed to be?

Nobody nose!

Your nose is packed with 400 different types of smell receptors, allowing you to recognize up to a trillion smells. This makes your nose more sensitive than your eyes, which can *only* detect several million different colours.

SPEAK UP!

Sssssh — don't tell anyone, but this page will give you SUPER HEARING! You'll also find out how your ears work.

CHALLENGE

Sit in a 'quiet' place like a park or library, and use your ear trumpet to listen in different directions. Make a 'sound map' of the noises you hear. Can you hear any sounds you've never noticed before?

Large ears help some animals to hear very faint sounds. Bat-eared foxes can hear insects crawling underground.

CHALLENGE

Try cupping your hand around one ear to make a human ear trumpet. Can you hear background sounds you don't normally notice? Does it make a difference if you cup your hands around both ears?

Sounds are made when objects vibrate. Sound can travel through ANY material that vibrates. It can travel much further and faster through a solid object like string than it can through air.

It sounds exactly like someone hitting a table with a coat hanger!

CHALLENGE 1

Extra kit:

- Scissors
- Wire coat hanger
- string

What to do:

1. Cut a 1-metre length of string.
2. Loop it through a wire coat hanger and hold the ends together.
3. Holding the string, swing the coat hanger gently against a wall or table. What can you hear?
4. Now, hold the ends of the string gently against both ears (don't poke anything into your ears). Swing the coat hanger so it bumps into the wall or table again. What does it sound like this time?

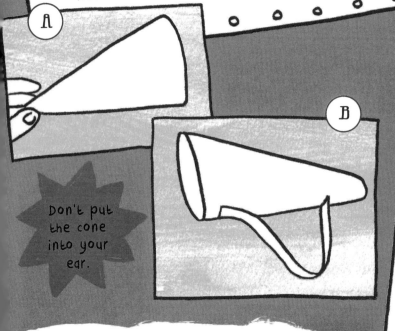

A

B

Don't put the cone into your ear.

Super hearing isn't so super if you have to be right next to the object making the sound. To listen in at a distance, you'll need a hearing trumpet.

CHALLENGE 2

Extra kit:

- A spare sheet of paper
- A strip of paper (2 cm wide, 20 cm long)
- A radio or music player
- Scissors
- Sticky tape

What to do:

1. Carefully roll the spare paper into a cone. Leave an opening of around 1 cm at the end. Make the other end as big as possible. Secure with a few pieces of sticky tape (A).
2. Stick the strip of paper on the cone, about 2 cm away from each end, to make a handle (B).
3. Turn the music player on and stand at the other end of the room. Ask a friend to slowly turn the volume down, stopping the moment you can't hear the music any more.
4. Hold the small opening of the cone to your ear and point the large opening at the music player. Can you hear the music now?
5. How far can you go with the cone and still hear the music? Can you hear as well if you point the cone in a different direction?

CHALLENGE

Try making larger cones with larger sheets of paper. Can you travel even further from the music player?

UPSIDE DOWN

Until telepathy is invented, your senses are the ONLY WAY to find out what's happening outside your own body. Sight is one of the most important senses. Unlike touch, taste and smell, your eyes can warn you what's going to happen BEFORE IT'S TOO LATE!

HANG ON, IT'S UPSIDE DOWN!

You're not seeing things — pictures really do hit the back of your eye the wrong way up. When light bounces off objects and into your eye, it travels through the clear cornea and lens. These bend and focus onto the retina — the surface of the back of your eye.

The retina is packed with sensitive cells, which change the image into signals that are sent to the brain. Your brain decodes the signals and flips the picture to make sense of what you are seeing. All this happens in MUCH less than the blink of an eye.

Extra kit:

- Scissors
- Scrap card e.g. an old cereal box
- Glue stick
- Paper fastener

What to do:

1. Cut page 37 out of the book and glue it to a sheet of thin card (illustrations facing upwards!). When the glue is dry, cut along the solid red and pink lines.

2. Use scissors to carefully poke a small hole in the two marked spots.

3. Tuck flap B behind the laughing dog. Push a paper fastener through the two holes to join the pieces.

4. Move tab C up and down to look at the dog. See how the image appears on your retina.

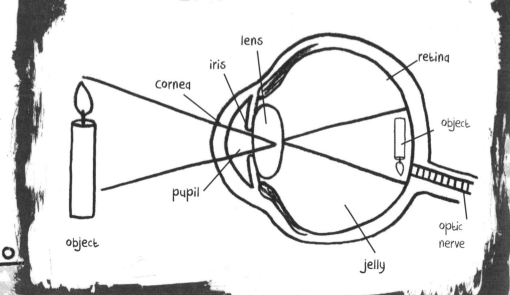

Cut out the shape
outlined in red.

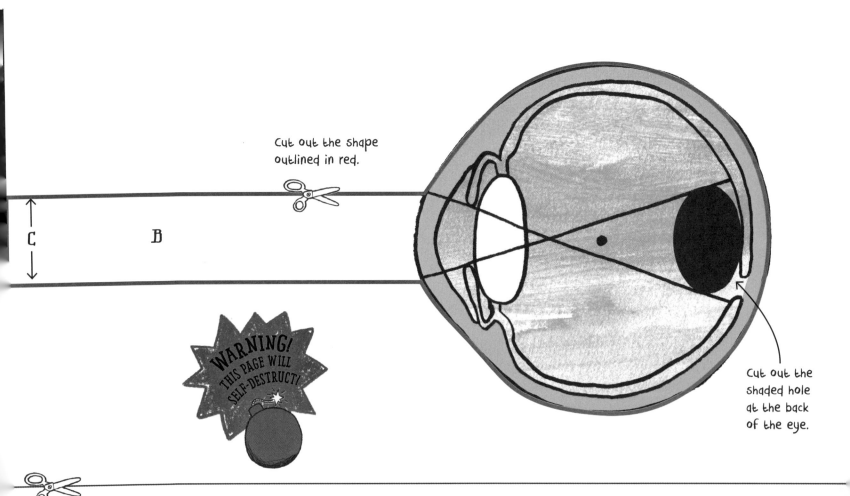

C

B

WARNING!
THIS PAGE WILL
SELF-DESTRUCT!

Cut out the
shaded hole
at the back
of the eye.

Cut around the lines outlined in pink. The dog's feet should still be attached to the page.

If you don't have sandpaper, use scraps of fabrics with different textures.

FEEL YOUR WAY

Your skin can detect heat, cold, pressure, and pain... but can it help you find your way through a maze?

Extra kit:

- Scissors
- Sticky tape and/or glue
- Six drinking straws
- Smooth grade sandpaper
- Rough grade sandpaper

What to do:

1. Carefully remove this page from the book and turn so the grid is facing upwards.

2. Stick lengths of drinking straw over each of the thick pink lines, to make the maze walls.

3. Cut out 16 squares of rough grade sandpaper, and 19 squares of smooth grade sandpaper. Each square should measure 3 cm x 3 cm. Glue the rough squares to the pink spaces, and the smooth squares to the white spaces.

4. Put the tip of your finger on 'Start'. Close your eyes and try to feel your way through the maze as quickly as possible, by following the smooth path.

5. Try again, this time using the back of your knuckle to feel your way.

When you touch something, receptors in your skin send messages to your brain. The brain uses the information to work out if you have touched something hot or cold, hard or soft, sticky or slimy.

Don't press too hard or you will sand your fingers!

WARNING! THIS PAGE WILL SELF-DESTRUCT!

Your fingertips are so sensitive they can feel bumps thinner than human hairs!

Your lips and tongue also have a high number of touch receptors but we DO NOT recommend that you lick your way through the maze!

Key:
• = touch receptor

HOW QUICKLY CAN YOU FIND YOUR WAY THROUGH?

RULES:
No looking   No listening
No smelling   No tasting

START

FINISH

KEY

Rough sandpaper

Smooth sandpaper

Was it easier to feel your way with your knuckle or fingertip?

MIND THE BURP

Join these corn kernels on a race through your digestive system. Watch out for the burp hazards!

Enzymes in saliva start to break down food into pieces too tiny to see.

Muscles squeeze food towards your stomach.

The stretchy stomach stores a litre of chewed food.

Tiny particles of carbohydrates, proteins, fats, vitamins and minerals pass through the wall of the small intestine.

Leftover material is stored until you visit the loo.

Billions of 'friendly' bacteria help your body to break down food.

Extra kit:
- Scissors
- Dice
- Counters

What to do:

1. Carefully cut this page out of the book, and place it on a flat surface, with the game board (page 42) facing up.

2. Find two counters and place them on the mouth.

3. Roll the dice to move, and follow the instructions on each square. If you land on a burp hazard, you get burped back up to the start again.

4. The first player to make it through the digestive system wins!

Your digestive system is a long tube. Food enters at your mouth and is crushed, dissolved and broken down so the good bits can be taken into your blood. Anything that isn't absorbed exits at the bottom!

Your digestive system breaks food into particles 10 million times smaller than a kernel of sweetcorn. It's a bit like breaking Mount Everest down into grains of sand!

OESOPHAGUS

MOUTH

Chewed by teeth – miss a turn

Squirted with saliva – move 2 spaces

BURP! You didn't chew your food

Squeezed towards the stomach – move 2 spaces

Attacked by acid – miss a turn

STOMACH

DUODENUM

BURP! Stomach too full

BURP! You ate too quickly

Bathed in bile – move 1 space

BURP! Gases form as food is broken down

Drenched in digestive juices – move 2 spaces

SMALL INTESTINE

Drenched in digestive juices – move 2 spaces

BURP! You swallowed air

APPENDI

Stuck in the appendix – miss 2 turns

Sucked dry – miss a turn

BURP! Too much fatty food

LARGE INTESTINE

BURP! Fizzy drink

BURP! You exercised after eating

I feel a little flushed!

FLUSHED AWAY
WINNER!

BURP! Indigestion

Sucked dry – miss a turn

Pushed out – move 2 spaces

RECTUM

COLON

BRAIN BENDERS

Your eyes can only take a snapshot of the sights around you. It's your brain's job to process the messages coming from your eyes, and work out what they mean. If your brain gets it wrong, you may 'see' something that isn't really there! Can you trick your brain using this page?

Extra kit:

· Pencil

What to do:

1. Hold a pencil and sit at arm's length from this book.

2. Close one eye and try to touch this dot with the pencil tip. •←

3. Most people miss the first time. Your brain will get better with practice, using clues from the first attempt.

Having two forward facing eyes helps you to see in 3D. By comparing the view from each eye, your brain works out what shape and how far away objects are. If you happen to be a Cyclops (or close one eye) your brain can't do this as well.

Optical illusions help scientists understand how our eyes and brain work together.

WARNING! THIS PAGE WILL SELF-DESTRUCT!

Extra kit:

· 1 spare piece of A4 paper

What to do:

1. Roll your spare piece of paper lengthways into a tube, around 1.5 cm across.

2. Hold the tube up to your left eye like a telescope.

3. Rest your right hand against the far end of the tube. Look at the palm with your right eye. What do you see?

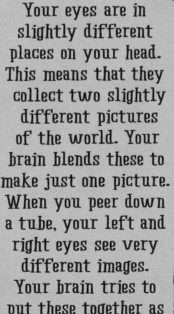

Your eyes are in slightly different places on your head. This means that they collect two slightly different pictures of the world. Your brain blends these to make just one picture. When you peer down a tube, your left and right eyes see very different images. Your brain tries to put these together as normal, creating a hole in your hand!

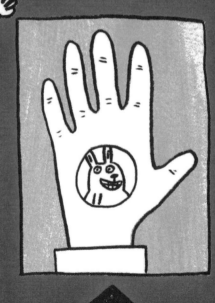

By showing each eye a slightly different flat image, you can trick your brain into seeing in 3D. Turn page 45 into a stereoscope to find out how.

Extra kit:
- Scissors
- Sticky tape

What to do:

1. Carefully cut page 45 out of the book. Cut along the solid lines (including the eye holes). Fold the sides inwards along the dotted lines, so each fold makes a right angle.

2. Tuck flaps A, B, C and D under the base to make a box shape. Tape them in place.

3. Cut out the rectangle of paper along the side of page 44. Fold this rectangle in half lengthways. Fold along the dotted line to make a flap.

4. Stick the flap into the bottom of the box you made in step 2 to create a 'wall' along the dotted line. Use sticky tape to secure the 'wall' in place, along the bottom, and also to the end with the eye holes.

5. Look through the eye holes. Relax your eyes, as if you were focusing on something much further away. Instead of seeing two different pictures, can you make your brain blend the images to see one 3D picture?

Between you and me, something smells.

GLUE

CHALLENGE
Get a glimpse of the view from both eyes by trying to look at your nose — you'll see two of everything!

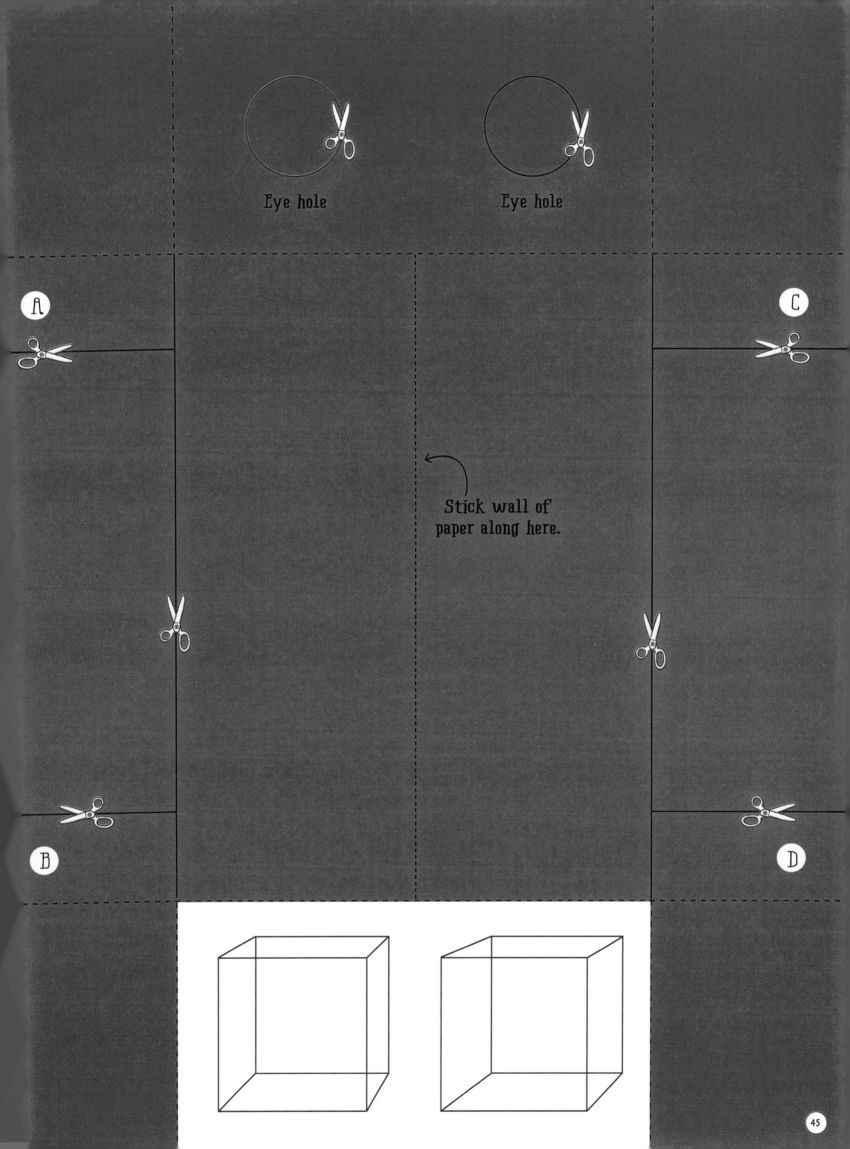

Eye hole

Eye hole

A

C

Stick wall of
paper along here.

B

D

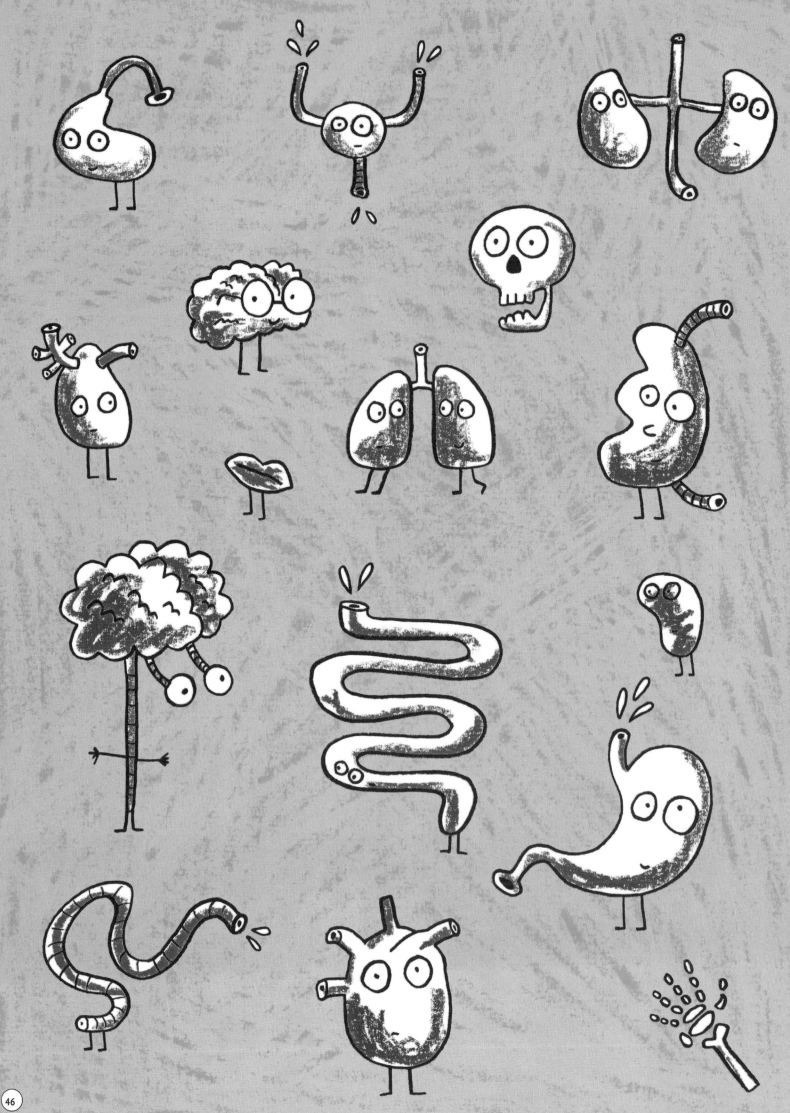

MAP YOUR TONGUE

Where are your taste buds, and what can they taste?
Set sail on a sea of saliva to create a map of your tongue.

Don't touch the very back of your tongue, or your breakfast may pop up to say hello!

Extra kit:

- Salt
- Sugar
- Lemon
- Cocoa or tonic water
- Soy sauce
- Water
- Cotton buds
- Five egg cups or small bowls
- Mirror

Ask an adult to help you gather the right foods.

What to do:

1. Put a teaspoon of each food into a different egg cup. Add a teaspoon of water to the sugar and salt cups, and mix well.

2. Dip a cotton bud into the cup of sugar water. Put a drop of the liquid on each area of your tongue in turn (tips, centre, sides, back). Try out the insides of your lips and cheeks too. Use the map on page 48 to record the places where the taste is strongest.

3. Take a sip of fresh water. Repeat step two with the other foods.

WHAT ARE TASTE BUDS?

Taste buds are tiny groups of cells that can detect five different tastes. When a sweet, salty, sour, bitter or umami chemical washes over a taste bud, particular cells get excited and send a message to your brain. Taste buds are found everywhere in your mouth, but most (around 5,000) are collected on your tongue. Each of the five tastes can be sensed ANYWHERE on your tongue.

Don't drink salt water!

YOUR TONGUE COULD SAVE YOUR LIFE

You may have spotted that the front, sides and back of your tongue are better than the middle at detecting all five tastes. Taste buds at the back of the tongue are especially good at detecting bitter tastes. Many poisonous substances taste bitter, so this helps you spit them out before they get swallowed! But it's best not to test this out!

KEY
▲ Sweet
● Sour
■ Salty
✖ Bitter
◆ Umami

ARE YOU A SUPERTASTER?

If you think green vegetables taste revolting, you may be a supertaster. Supertasters have up to twice the normal number of taste buds. They are super sensitive to bitter chemicals found in many green vegetables.

Back

I'm not a fussy eater, I'm SUPERTASTER!

Centre

Left side

Right side

If there are only five tastes, where do different flavours come from?

Your taste buds aren't actually THAT good at their job... most of what you 'taste' is down to your sense of smell. You can sniff out 10,000 different scents!

CHALLENGE

Trick your taste buds by holding your nose, and chewing grated apple and then grated onion. You won't be able to tell the difference – until chemicals from the onion drift into your nose. YUCK!

Tip

FINGERLYMPICS

Your bendy fingers and thumbs let you do all sorts of things that other animals can't — from throwing a ball to playing computer games. Find out just how fit your fingers are by staging a tabletop fingerlympics...

I don't even have a computer.

Extra kit:

- Scissors
- Colouring pens or pencils
- Clothes peg
- Timer
- Small empty box
- Computer keyboard
- Up to three extra competitors

What to do:

1. Colour and cut out the costumes on the inside of the back cover, making holes for your fingers. Give one to each competitor (you might need to take turns).

2. Warm up by practising each challenge. Just like real Olympic events, they test strength, speed, coordination and reaction time.

3. Stage your fingerlympics. Use the medal table below to record scores for each event. Who wins Gold, Silver and Bronze medals?

Try the events with your right AND your left hand. Do you notice a difference?

	Player 1	Player 2	Player 3	Player 4
Event 1				
Event 2				
Event 3				
Event 4				
Event 5				
Total score				

EVENT 1: FLYING CATCH

This event tests your reaction time – the time it takes for your nerves to carry a message from your eyes to your brain to your fingers!

1. Cut out the reaction time rule. (This is inside the back cover.)

2. Ask a friend to hold the rule at the top, so it hangs straight down.

3. Hold your thumb and first finger 1 cm apart, at the bottom of the rule.

4. When your friend drops the rule, catch it between your finger and thumb as quickly as possible!

5. Look at the rule to check your score. Write down your score in the table.

Messages are carried through your nerves at up to 120 metres per second - the speed of the world's fastest train!

What gets harder to catch the faster you run?

your breath!

EVENT 2: DIGITAL SPRINT

You'll need a computer keyboard for this event. Put your index finger on K, your middle finger on O, and your thumb on the space bar. How many times can you type the word OK in a minute? There must be a space between each word, and it must be spelled correctly. Record your score.

EVENT 3: THUMB MARATHON

Hold a clothes peg or bulldog clip between your first finger and thumb. How many times can you fully open and close it in one minute? Record your score – one point for each complete open and close.

WARNING! THIS PAGE WILL SELF-DESTRUCT!

I didn't expect this to be so tiring!

EVENT 4: MAZE RUNNER

This event tests how well you can control the hand you DON'T write with. Use a pencil to draw your way through the maze below as quickly as possible. Add a second to your score each time your pencil touches a line.

50 SECONDS 2 POINTS
40 SECONDS 4 POINTS
30 SECONDS 6 POINTS
20 SECONDS 8 POINTS
10 SECONDS 10 POINTS

Penalty spot

EVENT 5: FINGERBALL

Cut out the football and scrunch it into a tight ball. Place it on the penalty spot. Position a box or cup in the goal area. Try to score a goal by flicking the ball with your index finger. Record your score out of ten.

DREAM DIARY

After all that brain training, your brain deserves a rest. But a snooze might not be the answer...

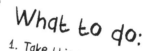

Extra kit:

· Pen or pencil

What to do:

1. Take this page out of the book and put it next to your bed. Each day for a month, doodle in the dream diary on page 54 to record the last dream you remember. Don't worry if you can't remember much – just record one picture or word. Draw an emoticon to show how it made you feel.

2. Your brain forgets dreams quickly, so fill in your dream diary first thing in the morning. If you can't remember dreaming at all, leave that box blank.

3. At the end of the month, compare your dream diary to a diary or calendar of your daily activities. Can you spot any patterns?

WHEN DO WE DREAM?

Your brain goes in and out of different types of sleep during the night. Most dreaming happens during a type of sleep called REM (Rapid Eye Movement) sleep. During REM sleep your brain can be even more active than when you are awake!
Your brain relaxes the rest of your muscles, so you don't act out your dreams.

CHALLENGE

Scientists have discovered that the LESS sleep we get, the MORE we dream the following night! Record how many hours' sleep you get in your dream diary. Can you spot any patterns?

Other mammals have REM sleep, so they probably dream too. In sea mammals such as dolphins, only half of the brain sleeps at a time. The other half stays awake so the dolphin can keep coming up to the surface to breathe!

Sorry, I was half asleep.

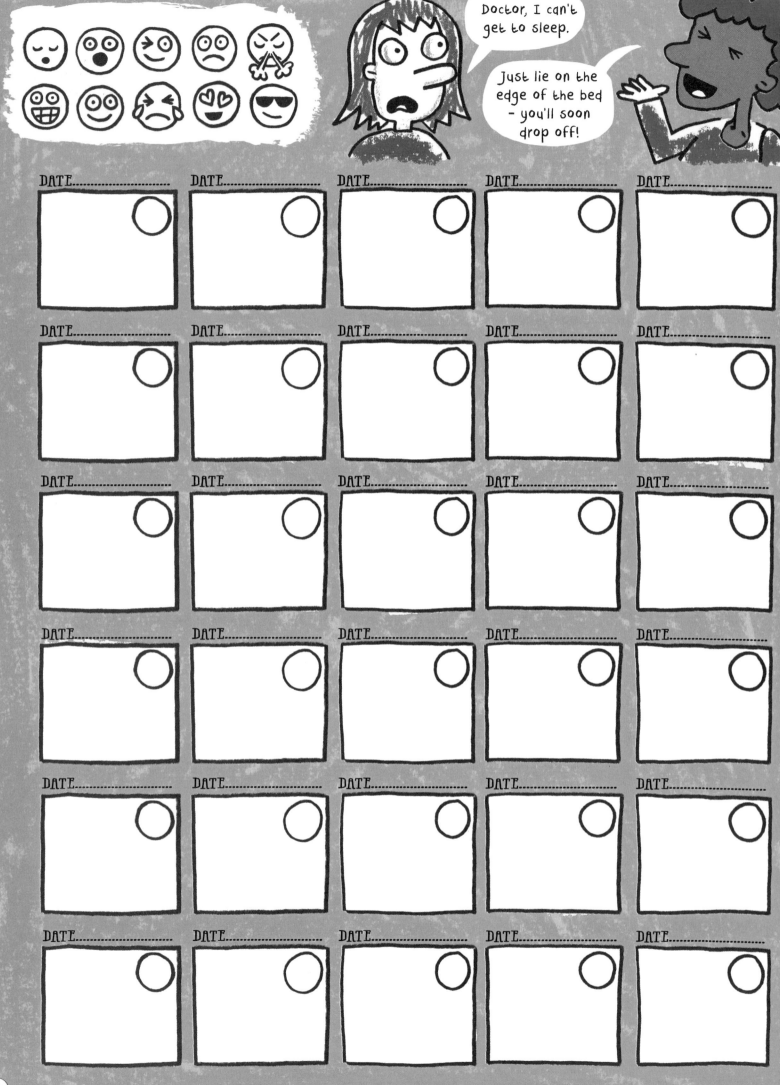

BALANCING ACT

Can you tiptoe in a straight line or hold yourself up in a handstand? Human brains are brilliant at keeping our bodies balanced. Learn how they do it, by helping this superhero take to the skies.

WARNING! THIS PAGE WILL SELF-DESTRUCT!

Extra kit:
- Scissors
- Two paperclips

What to do:

1. Cut out the superhero figure. Glue her to thin card and cut her out again.

2. Hold the superhero horizontally, and try balancing her nose on your fingertip. What happens?

3. Slide the paperclips on to different parts of the superhero. Can you position them so that she balances on her nose?

An object is balanced if it's not falling over. You are balanced right now. (unless you are falling over – in which case, PUT THE BOOK DOWN AND SAVE YOURSELF!)

Is it a bird? Is it a plane?

Next time you fall over, blame gravity. This force is constantly trying to pull every part of your body towards the ground. You can think of it as pulling down on a single point — your centre of gravity — somewhere near your belly button.

To stay balanced, your brain works hard to keep your centre of gravity over your feet.

CHALLENGE

1. Stand up straight and raise your right leg to the side. Your brain will tell your muscles to make small changes to bring your centre of gravity over your left foot. You might tighten some muscles, bend to one side, or stick an arm out.

2. Now, clear an area next to a wall and pad the floor for safety... you're about to mess with gravity!

3. Stand with your left foot and shoulder touching a wall and try raising your right foot again. This time the wall stops you moving your centre of gravity over your left foot, and you fall over!

Before you added paperclips to the superhero, her centre of gravity was somewhere near her belly button. Adding extra weight to her hands moves her centre of gravity to her nose — making this her new balancing point.

BODY ART

Make unique pictures using your fingerprints, handprints or lip prints. If anyone asks why you're kissing a book, just say it's art!

Why was the portrait sent to jail?

It was framed!

The artist's fingerprints were all over it!

Extra kit:
- Ink (or non-toxic face paints or make-up if you are planning to make lip prints)
- Pen or pencil

What to do:
1. Coat a fingertip in ink and press down firmly on the page to make a print. Try printing with different parts of your body too, to create different shapes and textures.

2. Turn your prints into art by doodling the details.

RECORD-BREAKING BODIES

From strange skills to serious sports, humans love to put their bodies to the test! How do you compare to these record-breakers?

MOST JUMPING JACKS IN A ROW: 27,000

_____
My score

MOST SKIPS IN 30 SECONDS: 108

_____
My score

Extra kit:
- Skipping rope
- Ruler
- Timer
- Socks
- Dice
- Coin
- Toilet rolls

What to do:
1. Clear an area and pad the floor for safety... you're about to test your limits!
2. Try each challenge and write your score in the box.

MOST JUMPING JACKS IN ONE MINUTE:
77

_____
My score

MOST TIME BALANCING ON ONE LEG:
76 HOURS 40 MINUTES

_____
My score

LARGEST HANDPRINT: 32.4 CM

_____
My score

LONGEST NUMBER MEMORIZED:
70,000 DIGITS

_____
My score

MOST SOCKS PUT ON A FOOT IN ONE MINUTE:
45

_____
My score

MOST DICE STACKED INTO A TOWER IN 30 SECONDS:
38

_____
My score

LONGEST TIME TO SPIN A COIN:
25.71 SECONDS

_____
My score

MOST FORWARD ROLLS IN 1 MINUTE:
75

_____
My score

TALLEST TOWER MADE OUT OF TOILET ROLLS, BUILT IN 30 SECONDS:
28 ROLLS

_____
My score

LONGEST TIME DOING KEEPY UPPY WHILE LYING ON THE FLOOR:
10 MINUTES 4 SECONDS

_____
My score

FAMILY TREE DETECTIVE

Fill in this family tree and find out exactly who to blame for your chin, ears, and even your taste buds!

1 2 3 4

KEY:
Shade the circle for each corresponding test (see page 61), if the answer is 'yes'!

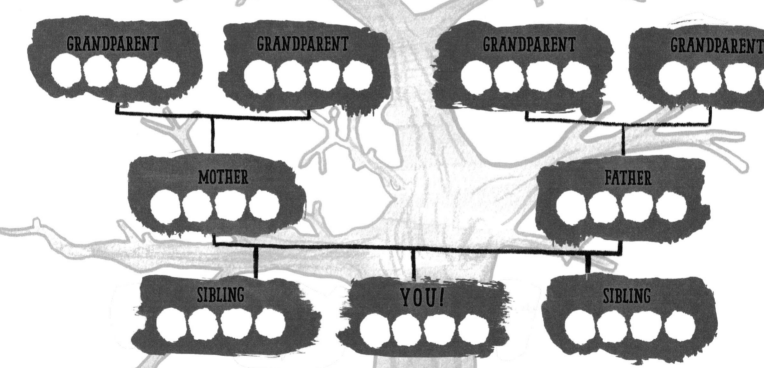

Add in more boxes if you need to!

When are genes inherited?

As soon as my sister grows out of them!

DOES IT RUN IN THE FAMILY?

We all have certain characteristics, or traits, that were passed on from our parents. These traits were passed on in our genes — the set of instructions that are used to build our bodies. We inherit half of our genes from our mother, and half from our father, so traits can be passed down from both sides of your family.

THE TESTS

You can use these tests on anyone. Test your friends to see how many traits you have in common! If you are testing your family members, record their answers by shading the boxes on the family tree.

1 TONGUE ROLL

Can you roll your tongue into a tube by curling up the sides?

Yes ◯   No ◯

This will really tie your tongue in knots: how much wood would a woodchuck chuck if a woodchuck could chuck wood?

2 DIMPLES

Do dimples appear on either of your cheeks when you smile?

Yes ◯   No ◯

3 FRECKLES

Do you have freckles?

Yes ◯   No ◯

CHIN SHAPE

Is your chin smooth, or does it have a dip in the middle (cleft chin)?

◯ Smooth

◯ Cleft

SHAPE OF HAIRLINE

Pull your hair back from your forehead. Does it form a straight line or a point (widow's peak)?

◯ Straight line

◯ Widow's peak

THUMBS UP!

Does your thumb stick straight up or bend backwards?

◯ Straight

◯ Bends back

Count Dracula famously had a widow's peak – but that doesn't mean everyone with a pointed hairline is a vampire!

A bendy thumb is known as a 'Hitchhiker's thumb'!

4 TASTE BUDS AT THE READY

Do broccoli and Brussels sprouts taste bitter to you?

◯ Yes

◯ No

If they do, it's because you've inherited a gene that lets you taste a chemical called PTC.

CLASPING HANDS

Clasp your hands by locking your fingers together. Which thumb is on top?

◯ Left thumb

◯ Right thumb

RED/GREEN COLOUR BLINDNESS

Can you see the colours red and green?

◯ Yes

◯ No

EARLOBES

Are your earlobes attached or detached?

◯ Attached

◯ Detached

THE SECRET OF LIFE

Have you ever wondered what the instruction manual for building YOU looks like? Make a model of your DNA and find out!

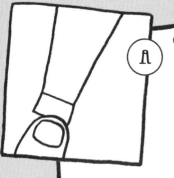

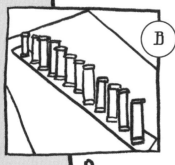

Extra kit:

- Scissors
- Sticky tape or glue
- Colouring pens or pencils
- Thread

What to do:

1. Cut out the 13 'rungs' on page 63.

2. Fold along the dotted lines to make a tab at both ends of each rung (A).

3. Cut out the two 'legs' on page 63.

4. Tape or glue the left-hand tab of each rung to leg 1, matching up the arrows (B).

5. If you used glue, wait for the first leg to dry. Tape or glue the other tab of each rung to leg 2, matching the coloured dots and arrows as before. You will have to twist each rung slightly. Don't worry – it's supposed to be wonky (C, D)!

6. When you've finished sticking all the tabs, the legs will curve around each other to form two spirals. This is a double helix (E)!

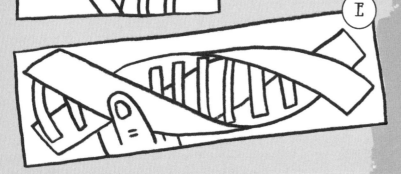

DNA is a chemical found in almost every cell in your body. Scientists were very excited when they discovered it looks just like a twisted ladder!

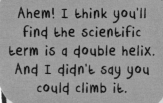

Ahem! I think you'll find the scientific term is a double helix. And I didn't say you could climb it.

If you hold each end of the double helix and twist, you will be able to coil it tightly and let it spring open again. Just like your paper double helix, DNA can coil up tightly when it is not being used.

LEG 1

LEG 2

Key

A:

C:

G:

T:

RUNGS

Make sure you work carefully and get each tab in the right place, or the results could be monstrous!

A, C, G and T stand for adenine, cytosine, guanine and thymine. These are four chemicals that pair up to make up the 'rungs' of the DNA ladder. Their order is very important. It forms a giant code — a recipe for making all the building blocks of your body.